Learn to Fold Origami

Holidays

Katie Gillespie

www.av2books.com

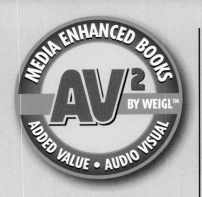

AV² provides enriched content that supplements and complements this Weigl's AV² books strive to create inspired learning and engage young r in a total learning experience.

Your AV² Media Enhanced books come alive with...

Audio
Listen to sections of the book read aloud.

Key Words
Study vocabulary, ar complete a matchin word activity.

Video
Watch informative video clips.

Quizzes
Test your knowledg

Go to **www.av2books.com**, and enter this book's unique code.

Embedded Weblinks
Gain additional information for research.

Slide Show
View images and captions, and prepar a presentation.

BOOK CODE

X 1 9 1 7 4 6

AV² **by Weigl** brings you media enhanced books that support active learning.

Try This!
Complete activities and hands-on experiments.

... and much, much m

Published by AV² by Weigl
350 5th Avenue, 59th Floor
New York, NY 10118
Website: www.weigl.com   www.av2books.com

Library of Congress Control Number: 2013953133

ISBN 978-1-4896-0648-8 (hardcover)
ISBN 978-1-4896-0649-5 (softcover)
ISBN 978-1-4896-0650-1 (single user eBook)
ISBN 978-1-4896-0651-8 (multi-user eBook)

Printed in the United States of America in North Mankato, Minnesota
1 2 3 4 5 6 7 8 9 0 17 16 15 14 13

122013
WEP301113

Senior Editor: Heather Kissock
Art Director: Terry Paulhus

Every reasonable effort has been made to trace ownership and to obtain permission to reprint copyright material. The publishers would be pleased to have any errors or omissions brought to their attention so that they may be corrected in subsequent printings.

Weigl acknowledges Getty Images as its primary image supplier for this title.

Origami patterns adapted from concepts originating with Fumiaki Shingu.

Contents

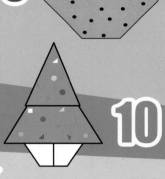

6

10

14

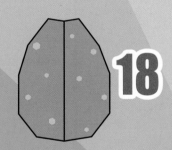

18

22

Be Mine

26

3

Why Fold Origami?

Origami is the Japanese art of paper folding. The Japanese, and the Chinese before them, have been folding paper into different **symbols** and designs for hundreds of years. The term "origami" comes from the Japanese words "ori," which means "folding," and "kami," which means "paper."

Paper used to be very expensive, so origami was an activity that only the rich could afford. Over time, paper became less expensive, and more people were able to participate in origami. Today, it is an art form that anyone can enjoy.

It is fun to make objects out of paper. Before you start doing origami, there are three basic folds that you must learn. Knowing these three folds will help you create almost any simple origami model.

Hood Fold
Hood folds are often used to make holiday symbols. To make a hood fold, fold along the dotted line, and crease. Then, unfold the paper. Open the pocket you have created. Flip the paper inside out along the creases, and flatten.

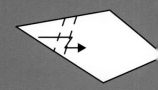

Pocket Fold
Pocket folds are often used to make other holiday symbols. To make a pocket fold, fold along the dotted line, and crease. Then, unfold the paper. Open the pocket you have created. Fold the point inside along the creases, and flatten.

Step Fold
Step folds are often used to make other parts of holiday symbols. To make a step fold, fold backward along the dotted line, and crease. Then, fold frontward along the dotted line, and crease. Repeat as necessary.

You will need:
- Origami paper
- Colored markers or crayons

Practice making your favorite holiday symbols in this book to learn the skills needed to fold origami.

Holidays

A holiday is a special time. Some holidays take place in a single day. Others go on for weeks. Most holidays are rooted in **customs** that date back many years. These customs can be based on religion, **cultural** traditions, or historical events.

Holidays are important. They allow us to learn about the beliefs of people from the past. They can also teach us about other cultures. Holidays give us a chance to spend time with loved ones. Sharing food, stories, and music are all ways to enjoy a holiday. Holidays also give us the opportunity to learn about the world.

As you fold the origami models in this book, think about the symbols associated with each holiday. Where did they come from? Why are they important?

What Is Chinese New Year?

T he Chinese New Year's celebration is one of the most important holidays for the Chinese. The holiday has been observed for centuries. The exact date of the holiday changes every year. However, it always begins on the first day of the first **lunar month** of the Chinese calendar, which occurs in late January or early February. The celebration lasts for 15 days, but preparation for the holiday may take weeks.

Certain foods have a special meaning to the Chinese. New Year's is the time for oranges and tangerines. These fruits are often given as gifts to children and guests. People associate these fruits with wealth and good luck.

Leaves
The Chinese use oranges and tangerines in New Year's displays. The fruits are often shown with their leaves attached. This is because leaves stand for **longevity** in Chinese culture.

Taste
Oranges are a sweet fruit. Eating them at New Year's is a treat. It is believed they will bring sweetness in the coming year.

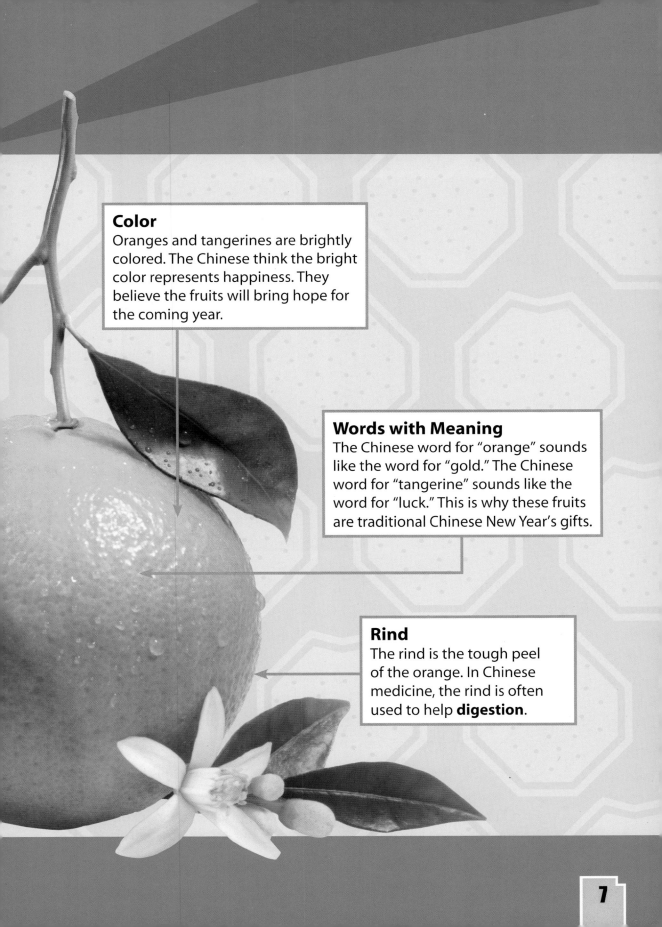

Color
Oranges and tangerines are brightly colored. The Chinese think the bright color represents happiness. They believe the fruits will bring hope for the coming year.

Words with Meaning
The Chinese word for "orange" sounds like the word for "gold." The Chinese word for "tangerine" sounds like the word for "luck." This is why these fruits are traditional Chinese New Year's gifts.

Rind
The rind is the tough peel of the orange. In Chinese medicine, the rind is often used to help **digestion**.

How to Fold an
Orange

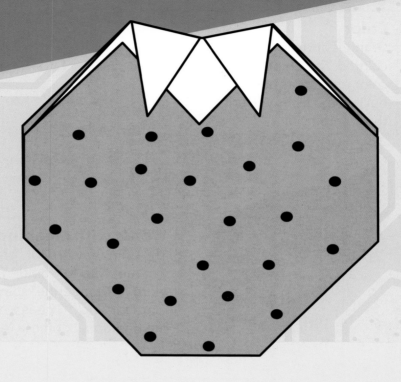

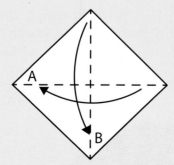

1 Fold in half along line A. Then, fold in half along line B.

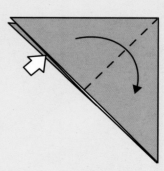

2 Open the pocket at the white arrow, and flatten.

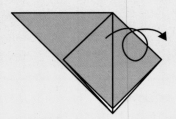

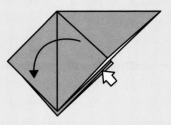

3 Turn the orange over.

4 Open the pocket at the white arrow, and flatten.

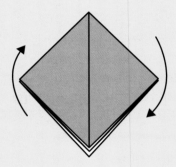

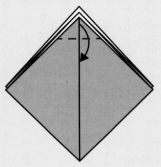

5 Turn the orange, as shown.

6 Fold the front flap down along the dotted line. Repeat on the back flap.

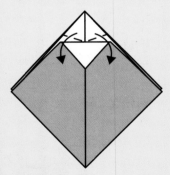

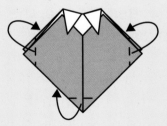

7 Fold forward along the top left dotted line, as shown. Repeat on the right side.

8 Fold backward along the bottom point, as shown. Repeat on the left and right points.

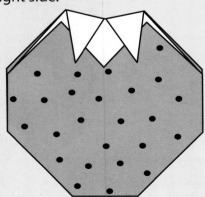

9 Finish the orange by drawing its spots.

What Is Christmas?

Christmas is one of the most popular holidays in the United States. It is also an important religious celebration. This holiday celebrates the birth of Jesus Christ. **Christians** believe that Jesus was the son of God.

Christmas is celebrated every year on December 25, but celebrations take place throughout the month. Today, the holiday includes both Christian customs and those from other winter festivals. Decorating a Christmas tree is one of the most popular customs.

The custom of decorating Christmas trees began in the early 1600s. According to legend, one Christmas night, a German man noticed how lovely the evergreen trees looked in the starlight. He cut down a small tree. Then, he took it home and decorated it with candles. Soon, Christmas trees were a popular way to mark the Christmas season.

Tinsel and Garlands

Many people decorate their trees with thin strips of metallic paper called tinsel. The tinsel represents icicles. In the winter, icicles often hang from trees. Trees are also decorated with garlands made of ribbon and other materials, such as berries or holly. Garlands are wrapped around a Christmas tree in a circular pattern. This pattern represents eternity.

Lights

Christians believe that lights represent the light that Jesus Christ brought to the world. Today, families decorate Christmas trees with electric lights instead of candles. Electric lights are much safer because they reduce the risk of fire.

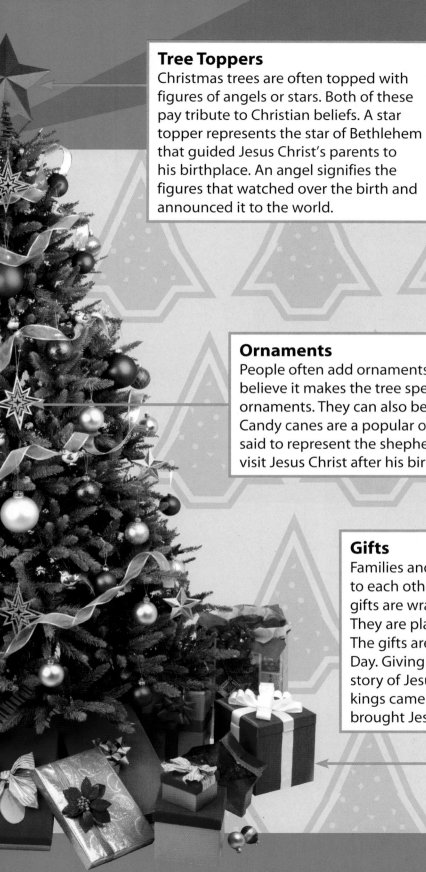

Tree Toppers

Christmas trees are often topped with figures of angels or stars. Both of these pay tribute to Christian beliefs. A star topper represents the star of Bethlehem that guided Jesus Christ's parents to his birthplace. An angel signifies the figures that watched over the birth and announced it to the world.

Ornaments

People often add ornaments to their tree. They believe it makes the tree special. People can buy ornaments. They can also be made at home. Candy canes are a popular ornament. They are said to represent the shepherds that came to visit Jesus Christ after his birth.

Gifts

Families and friends often give gifts to each other at Christmas. The gifts are wrapped in festive paper. They are placed under the tree. The gifts are opened on Christmas Day. Giving gifts also relates to the story of Jesus. After his birth, three kings came to visit him. Each king brought Jesus a gift.

How to Fold a
Christmas Tree

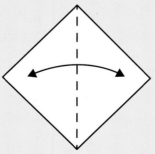

1 Fold in half along the dotted line, and crease. Open the paper.

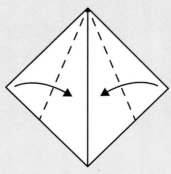

2 Fold the left side in along the dotted line to meet the center line. Repeat on the right side.

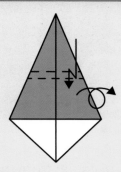

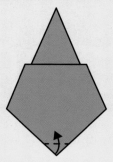

3 Step fold along the dotted lines, as shown. Then, turn over the tree.

4 Fold the bottom point up along the dotted line, as shown.

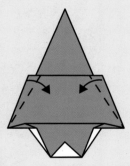

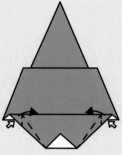

5 Step fold along the dotted lines, as shown.

6 Open the left pocket at the white arrow, and flatten. Repeat on the right pocket.

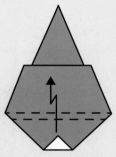

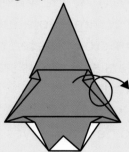

7 Fold along the left dotted line, as shown. Repeat on the right side.

8 Turn over the tree.

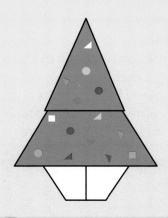

9 Finish the tree by drawing its decorations.

What Is Cinco de Mayo?

Cinco de Mayo is a holiday in both Mexico and the United States. The words *Cinco de Mayo* are Spanish. They mean "fifth of May." This holiday celebrates the Mexican army's winning the Battle of Puebla. This fight between the Mexican and French armies took place on May 5, 1862, near the city of Puebla, Mexico. At the time, France was trying to take over the government of Mexico and had sent its army to invade Mexico. The holiday commemorating this military victory started more than 100 years ago and is still celebrated today.

Today, Cinco de Mayo gives people the chance to get together to learn about and celebrate Mexican culture. They eat Mexican food and dance to Mexican music. Some people wear traditional Mexican clothing. They may wear a hat called a sombrero.

Brim
The word "sombrero" comes from the Spanish word *sombra*. In English, the word means "shade." Sombreros are known for their wide brims. Many workers spent most of their day in the hot sun. This brim protected the wearer from the Sun.

Material
Sombreros can be made of straw. They can also be made of felt or velvet. The hats come in many bright colors and patterns. Some sombreros are decorated with sequins and elaborate designs.

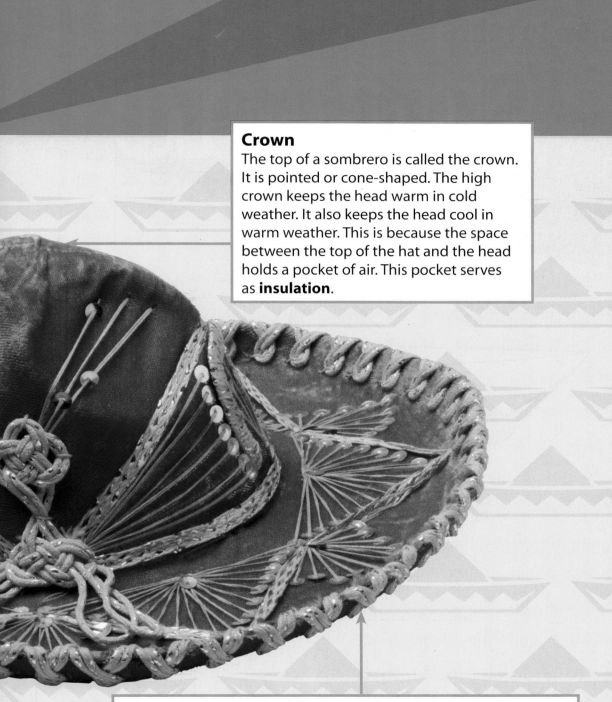

Crown

The top of a sombrero is called the crown. It is pointed or cone-shaped. The high crown keeps the head warm in cold weather. It also keeps the head cool in warm weather. This is because the space between the top of the hat and the head holds a pocket of air. This pocket serves as **insulation**.

Mexican Hat Dance

Cinco de Mayo is often celebrated with a **fiesta**. At the fiesta, some people perform the Mexican Hat Dance. The Mexican Hat Dance is the national folk dance of Mexico. It tells a story of love. A man and a woman perform the dance. The hat the dancers use is the sombrero. At the end of the dance, the female dancer puts the hat over their faces. This gives them privacy to share a kiss.

How to Fold a
Sombrero

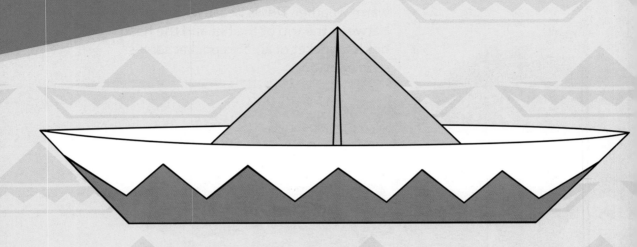

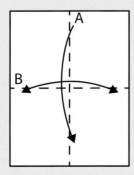

1 Fold in half along line A. Open the paper. Then, fold in half along line B.

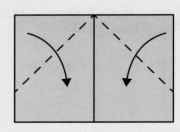

2 Fold down along the left dotted line, as shown. Repeat on the right side.

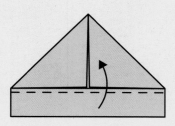

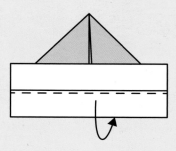

3 Fold the front flap up along the dotted line, as shown.

4 Fold the flap backward along the dotted line, as shown.

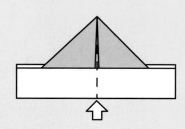

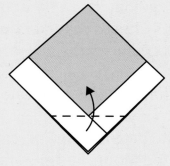

5 Open the pocket at the white arrow, and flatten.

6 Fold the front flap up along the dotted line. Repeat for the back flap.

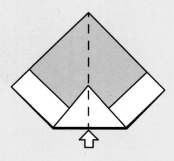

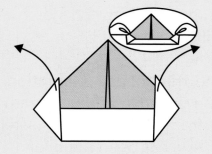

7 Open the pocket at the white arrow and flatten.

8 Make the sombrero's brim by pulling out the tips, as shown.

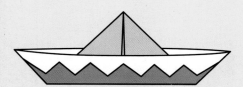

9 Finish the sombrero by drawing its pattern.

What Is Easter?

E aster is a celebration of spring. The holiday also celebrates new life. For Christians, Easter is an important holiday. It is a time to honor Jesus Christ's **resurrection** almost 2,000 years ago.

The date that Easter is celebrated changes from year to year. This is because the date is based on the phases of the Moon. Easter is always celebrated on the Sunday that follows the first full moon of spring. This means that millions of people throughout the world celebrate Easter sometime between March 22 and April 25.

Over time, this holiday celebration has mixed Christian traditions with customs from other cultures. Easter egg painting has been done for years. Before Jesus Christ was born, people painted eggs to celebrate the arrival of spring. The tradition continues to this day.

A New Life

Many creatures begin their lives as an egg. Over time, eggs have become a symbol for new life, **fertility**, and rebirth. Eggs play a role in the Easter tradition. They also represent the arrival of spring. This is the time of year when plants bloom and animals give birth to their babies.

Shape

The Easter egg's oval shape is said to stand for eternity. This is because there is no beginning and no end to an oval.

Dye

Dyeing eggs is another way to celebrate rebirth and renewal. Easter eggs can be quite colorful. Some are dyed with solid colors. Others have patterns put on them. Ukrainian Easter eggs are known for their extremely elaborate designs. First, wax is carefully applied to the egg. Then, it is dyed. This process is repeated until the pattern is complete.

Shell

To Christians, the hard shell of an egg represents the **tomb** where Jesus Christ was laid to rest when he died. Cracking the shell represents the rebirth of Jesus Christ.

How to Fold an Easter Egg

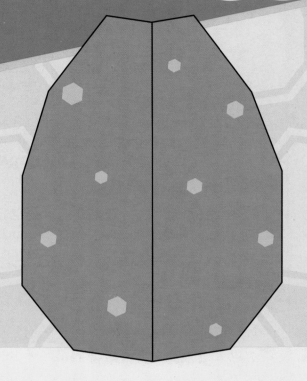

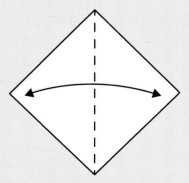

1 Fold in half along the dotted line, and crease. Open the paper.

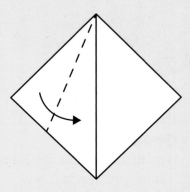

2 Fold the left side in to meet the center line, as shown.

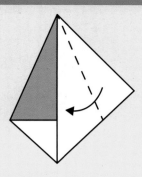

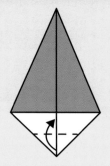

3 Fold the right side in to meet the center line.

4 Fold the bottom point up along the dotted line, as shown.

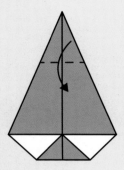

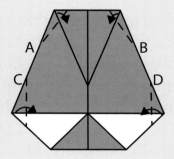

5 Fold the top point down along the dotted line, as shown.

6 Fold in along lines A, B, C, and D, as shown.

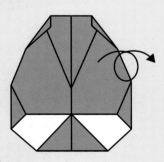

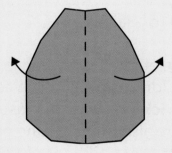

7 Turn the Easter egg over.

8 Fold in half, and crease. Open the paper so the Easter egg stands up.

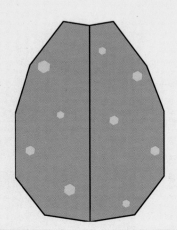

9 Finish your Easter egg by decorating it.

What Is Halloween?

Halloween is a holiday that is celebrated in many countries around the world. It started from a **Celtic** festival called Samhain that dates back to about the 5th century BC. The festival was held to celebrate the end of summer. In the 7th century AD, the Catholic Church began celebrating some of its holy days around the same time. "All Saints Day," also known as "All Hallows Day," took place on November 1. This made the day before, October 31, "All Hallows Eve." Over time, the name changed to "Halloween."

People celebrate Halloween in many ways. Children often dress in costumes and go **trick-or-treating**. Costume parties are also popular. One of the most common traditions of Halloween is the carving of pumpkins to make jack-o'-lanterns. Jack-o'-lanterns are put in windows and on front porches to greet trick-or-treaters.

Fruit or Vegetable
The jack-o'-lantern is named after a mysterious light that sometimes shines over the **peat bogs** of Ireland. In the past, jack-o'-lanterns were made out of turnips. In England, large beets are used. Most people in the United States carve pumpkins into jack-o'-lanterns.

Shell

The key part of a jack-o'-lantern is its carved face. Faces can be funny or scary. The first jack-o'-lanterns had scary faces. It is believed that they were used to scare off evil **spirits**. People would carve a scary face into the shell. They would put a lighted candle inside. Then, they left the glowing pumpkin in their window.

Candle

After the pulp is removed, a candle is placed inside the pumpkin shell. At night, the candle is lit. The light from inside shows off the carved face of the pumpkin. Today, people often use flashlights instead of candles to light their pumpkins.

Pulp

To make a jack-o'-lantern, people cut off the top of the pumpkin. Then, they remove the pumpkin **pulp**. This leaves only the shell. The pulp can be used to make pies and muffins.

How to Fold a
Jack-o'-Lantern

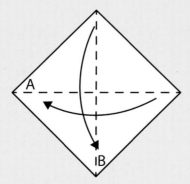

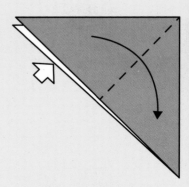

1. Fold in half along line A. Then, fold in half along line B.

2. Fold along the dotted line, as shown, and crease. Open the pocket at the white arrow, and flatten.

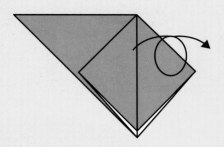

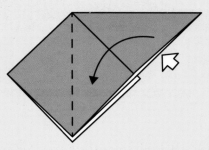

3 Turn over the jack-o'-lantern.

4 Fold along the dotted line, as shown, and crease. Open the pocket at the white arrow, and flatten.

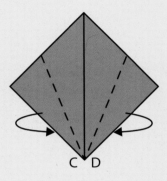

C D

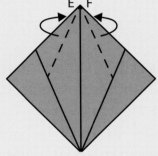

E F

5 Fold backward along lines C and D, as shown.

6 Fold backward along lines E and F, as shown.

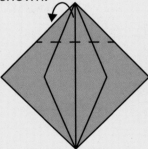

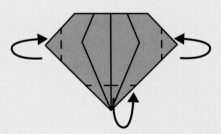

7 Fold backward along the dotted line, as shown.

8 Fold backward along the bottom point, as shown. Repeat on the left and right points.

9 Finish the jack-o'-lantern by drawing its face.

What Is Valentine's Day?

Valentine's Day celebrates love and friendship. It gives people the chance to tell others that they care about them. Each year on February 14, people send each other greeting cards, flowers, and candy to show their love.

Valentine's Day is named for St. Valentine, who lived hundreds of years ago in Rome. Valentine is best known for marrying couples in secret. This happened at a time when marriage engagements were forbidden by the Roman emperor Claudius II. The emperor found out what Valentine was doing, and Valentine was sentenced to death. He died on February 14, probably in the year 270 AD. This is why people celebrate Valentine's Day on February 14.

One of the most famous symbols of Valentine's Day is the heart. In ancient times, the heart was believed to be the source of human emotion. Over time, the heart has become a symbol of love. Most Valentine's Day gifts feature hearts to show the purpose of the holiday.

Shape

A Valentine's Day heart looks very different from the human heart. There are many **theories** about the shape of the Valentine's Day heart. Some people say it looks like the human **torso**. Others say it looks like an arrowhead. This refers to Cupid, the Roman god of love. Cupid shot arrows into people to make them fall in love.

Color

Most Valentine's Day cards feature hearts. The hearts are colored red or pink. The color red often represents passion and love. Pink is often said to represent friendship and affection.

The Gift of the Heart

The Valentine's Day tradition of giving heart-shaped presents is symbolic. The gifts are supposed to show that people are willing to give up their lives for the person they love.

How to Fold a Valentine Heart

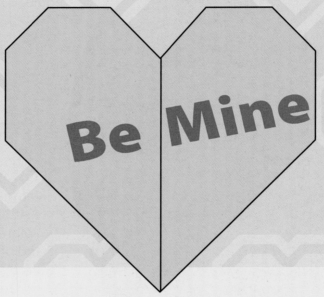

Be Mine

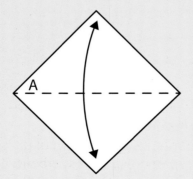

1 Fold in half along line A, and crease. Open the paper.

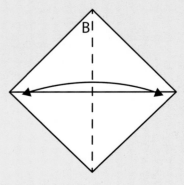

2 Fold in half along line B, and crease. Open the paper.

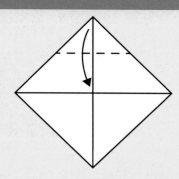

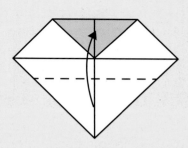

3 Fold the top point down along the dotted line, as shown.

4 Fold the bottom point up along the dotted line, as shown.

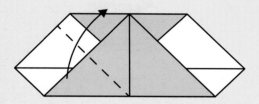

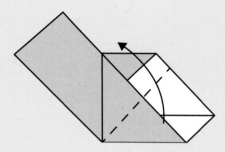

5 Fold along the dotted line to meet the center.

6 Fold along the dotted line to meet the center.

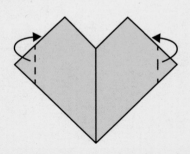

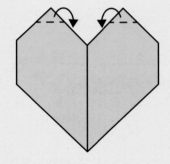

7 Fold the left point backward, as shown. Repeat on the right side.

8 Fold the top left point down, as shown. Repeat on the top right point.

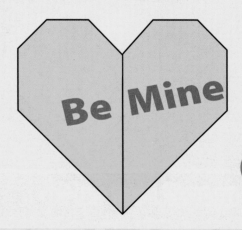

9 Finish your Valentine heart by decorating it.

Test Your Knowledge of Holidays

1. Why do people give oranges as gifts during Chinese New Year?

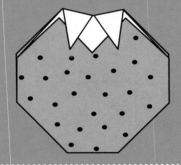

Answer: Oranges are associated with wealth and good luck.

2. Where did Christmas trees originate?

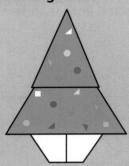

Answer: Germany

3. What does Cinco de Mayo celebrate?

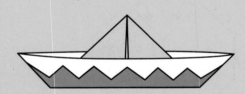

Answer: The victory of the Mexican army at the Battle of Puebla

4. When is Easter celebrated?

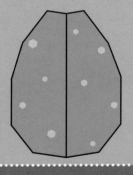

Answer: On the Sunday following the first full moon of spring

5. What were jack-o'-lanterns originally carved from?

Answer: Turnips

6. Why are Valentine's Day hearts often red?

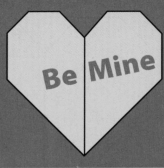

Be Mine

Answer: Because red is the color that represents love and passion

30

Want to learn more? Log on to www.av2books.com to access more content.

Holiday Sugar Cookies

Materials

2 cups all-purpose flour
½ teaspoon baking powder
¼ teaspoon salt
½ cup unsalted butter
1 cup granulated sugar
1 large egg
1 teaspoon vanilla extract

- Assorted candies, sprinkles, icing, etc.
- 2 large bowls
- Whisk and/or wooden spoon
- Plastic wrap
- Baking sheet
- Rolling pin
- Cookie cutters

Steps

1. In one large bowl, whisk together the flour, baking powder, and salt. In the other bowl, cream the butter and sugar. Whisk in the egg and vanilla.
2. Slowly add the flour mixture to the wet ingredients. Mix until combined.
3. Divide the dough in half, and flatten into disks. Wrap the dough in plastic, and freeze for 20 minutes.
4. With adult supervision, preheat the oven to 325 degrees. Remove the dough from the freezer. Let it stand for 5 to 10 minutes. Roll the dough out 1/8 inch thick, dusting it with flour if needed.
5. Cut the dough into shapes using the cookie cutters. Place the dough on the baking sheets. Bake for 10 to 18 minutes, until the edges are golden.
6. Let the cookies cool. Then, decorate with icing and candies.

Key Words

Celtic: belonging to a group of people who lived in Ireland and Scotland

Christians: people who follow the teachings of Jesus Christ

cultural: relating to the beliefs of a certain group of people

customs: traditions that people always perform

digestion: breaking down for use by the body

fertility: the ability to produce young

fiesta: a celebration or party

insulation: protection from the weather

longevity: long life

lunar month: the time between new or full moons

peat bogs: areas of wet, spongy ground

pulp: the soft, wet filling of something

resurrection: the rebirth of someone who has died

spirits: supernatural beings

symbols: objects that stand for something else

theories: ideas that explain why something happens

tomb: a structure where a dead body is placed

torso: the part of the human body between the legs and neck

trick-or-treating: visiting houses on Halloween to play a trick or ask for candy

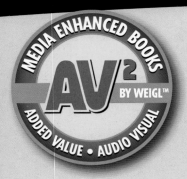

Log on to www.av2books.com

AV² by Weigl brings you media enhanced books that support active learning. Go to www.av2books.com, and enter the special code found on page 2 of this book. You will gain access to enriched and enhanced content that supplements and complements this book. Content includes video, audio, weblinks, quizzes, a slide show, and activities.

AV² Online Navigation

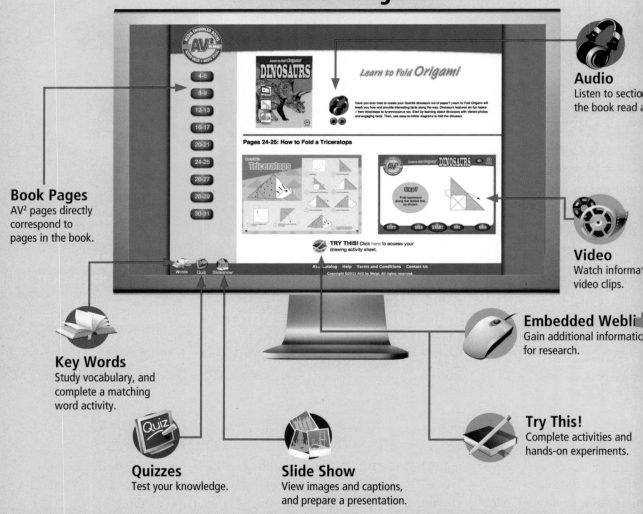

Audio
Listen to section the book read

Video
Watch informa video clips.

Embedded Webli
Gain additional informatic for research.

Try This!
Complete activities and hands-on experiments.

Book Pages
AV² pages directly correspond to pages in the book.

Key Words
Study vocabulary, and complete a matching word activity.

Quizzes
Test your knowledge.

Slide Show
View images and captions, and prepare a presentation.

AV² was built to bridge the gap between print and digital. We encourage you to tell us what you like and what you want to see in the future.

Sign up to be an AV² Ambassador at www.av2books.com/ambassador.

Due to the dynamic nature of the Internet, some of the URLs and activities provided as part of AV² by Weigl may have changed or ceased to exist. AV² by Weigl accepts no responsibility for any such changes. All media enhanced books are regularly monitored to update addresses and sites in a timely manner. Contact AV² by Weigl at 1-866-649-3445 or av2books@weigl.com with any questions, comments, or feedback.